THE BOOK OF Joshua

ONE CHAPTER A DAY

GoodMorningGirls.org

Welcome to Good Morning Girls! We are so glad you are joining us.

God created us to walk with Him, to know Him, and to be loved by Him. He is our living well, and when we drink from the water He continually provides, His living water will change the entire course of our lives.

Jesus said: "Whoever drinks of the water that I will give him will never be thirsty again. The water that I will give him will become in him a spring of water welling up to eternal life." ~ John 4:14 (ESV)

So let's begin.

The method we use here at GMG is called the **SOAK** method.

- ❒ **S**—The S stands for *Scripture*—Read the chapter for the day. Then choose 1-2 verses and write them out word for word. (There is no right or wrong choice—just let the Holy Spirit guide you.)

- ❒ **O**—The O stands for *Observation*—Look at the verse or verses you wrote out. Write 1 or 2 observations. What stands out to you? What do you learn about the character of God from these verses? Is there a promise, command or teaching?

- ❒ **A**—The A stands for *Application*—Personalize the verses. What is God saying to you? How can you apply them to your life? Are there any changes you need to make or an action to take?

- ❒ **K**—The K stands for *Kneeling in Prayer*—Pause, kneel and pray. Confess any sin God has revealed to you today. Praise God for His word. Pray the passage over your own life or someone you love. Ask God to help you live out your applications.

SOAK God's word into your heart and squeeze every bit of nourishment you can out of each day's scripture reading. Soon you will find your life transformed by the renewing of your mind!

Walk with the King!

Courtney

WomenLivingWell.org, GoodMorningGirls.org

Join the GMG Community

*Share your daily SOAK at 7:45am on **Facebook.com/GoodMorningGirlsWLW***

Instagram: WomenLivingWell #GoodMorningGirls

GMG Bible Coloring Chart

COLORS	KEYWORDS
PURPLE	God, Jesus, Holy Spirit, Saviour, Messiah
PINK	women of the Bible, family, marriage, parenting, friendship, relationships
RED	love, kindness, mercy, compassion, peace, grace
GREEN	faith, obedience, growth, fruit, salvation, fellowship, repentance
YELLOW	worship, prayer, praise, doctrine, angels, miracles,power of God, blessings
BLUE	wisdom, teaching, instruction, commands
ORANGE	prophecy, history, times, places, kings, genealogies, people, numbers, covenants, vows, visions, oaths, future
BROWN/GRAY	Satan, sin, death, hell, evil, idols, false teachers, hypocrisy, temptation

Introduction to the Book of Joshua

What makes a good leader? God's Word gives us examples of both good and bad ones. Some leaders come into their role naturally, others are appointed - or it might even be thrust upon them. Some are good, and look after the well being of their followers, while others are in it for selfish gain.

God is the ultimate leader. The Israelites had spent 40 years wandering aimlessly because they were not good at "following the leader" and obeying God. Finally, the new generation had risen and it was time to cross the Jordan and possess the land God had promised to them.

Joshua was a natural leader. His character had set him apart from the rest. This book, named after the man himself, records his leadership of the children of Israel into the land of Canaan - finally, home in the Promised Land.

This book is broken into two main parts. The first is a narrative of events surrounding the conquest of Canaan. The second part is the assignment and settlement of the land. It concludes with Joshua's farewell speech.

Joshua was committed to obeying God and obedience is a central theme of the book. It is the central theme of Joshua's life and his final charge (Joshua 24:15).

As we read the book of Joshua, lets make a commitment - a commitment to obey the Words of the Lord. Let's commit to follow where He leads, and be the kind of leader that brings others into His Kingdom.

Purpose: To give the history of Israel's conquest of the Promised Land.

Author: It is assumed Joshua wrote this entire book, except for the end. Commentaries say, that the high priest, who was an eyewitness of these events might, have written the ending.

Time Period: The precise time is not clear. An estimate is 1050 BC.

Key Verse: "Have I not commanded you? Be strong and courageous. Do not be frightened, and do not be dismayed, for the Lord your God is with you wherever you go." Joshua 1:9

The Outline:

1. **Entering the Promise Land (1:1-5:12)**

   Joshua demonstrated his faith in God as he took up the challenge to lead the nation. Israel re-confirms their commitment to God and their obedience as they cross over the Jordan. For us, we need to cross from our old life, to our new life in Jesus Christ. We need to put off our old selfish desires and possess all God has planned for us. This will require us to conquer some strongholds in our life, just as Israel conquered the nations that were in the Promised Land. We need courage to live this life of faith.

2. **Conquering the Promised Land (5:13-12:24)**

   Joshua and his army moved from city to city conquering the land and destroying evil. We too need to conquer the evil and strongholds in our lives.

3. **Dividing the Promised Land (13:1-24:33)**

   Joshua pleads with Israel to worship God alone and to follow the example that Joshua has left. They have seen the mighty hand of God at work but they were prone to wandering. We have seen God work in our lives, yet our hearts still wander. We must renew our commitment to love and obey Him above all else.

Themes:

Faith: The children of Israel demonstrated their faith in God daily to save and guide them. They looked at how God had been faithful in the past to help them stay focused in the present. We can have strength to follow God as we remember His promises. Faith starts with believing He can be trusted.

Leadership: Joshua is a clear picture of Jesus Christ. He is also an example of an excellent leader. He was confident in the Lord and obeyed His voice. To be a strong leader, we must be ready to listen and obey. Strong leaders are good followers of God.

Conquest: God commanded his people to conquer Canaan. This was to be a fulfillment of the promise that God made to Abraham. They were to do it completely but they never finished the task. We too need to be willing to conquer sin and evil in our lives, and continue to work at it until the job is finished.

I'm so excited to begin the book of Joshua with you. We are about to embark on a wonderful journey as we see the wonders of God's hand through the parting of the Jordan, the walls of Jericho falling and the sun standing still. May we stand in awe at the powerful God we serve.

Keep walking with the King!

Special Thanks

I want to extend a special thank you to Mandy Kelly, Rosilind Jukic, Bridget Childress and Misty Leask for your help with this journal. Your love, dedication and leadership to the Good Morning Girls ministry is such a blessing to all. Thank you for giving to the Lord.

~ Courtney

Have I not commanded you?

Be strong and courageous.

Do not be frightened, and do not be dismayed,

for the Lord your God is with you wherever you go

Joshua 1:9

Reflection Question:

Throughout the reading, the Israelites are reminded to be strong and courageous.

What is something that you are dealing with today that requires you to be strong and courageous?

S—The S stands for *Scripture*

O—The O stands for *Observation*

A—The A stands for *Application*

K—The K stands for *Kneeling in Prayer*

For the Lord your God,

He is God in the heavens above

And on the earth beneath.

Joshua 2:11

Reflection Question:

Rahab stepped out in faith to help the spies.

Name a time you had to step out in faith for God.

S—The S stands for **Scripture**

O—The O stands for **Observation**

A—The A stands for **Application**

K—The K stands for **Kneeling in Prayer**

Consecrate yourselves,

for tomorrow the Lord

will do wonders among you.

Joshua 3:5

Reflection Question:

God used a miracle to show Joshua and all of Israel that He was with them.

How has God shown you that he is with you?

S—The S stands for *Scripture*

O—The O stands for *Observation*

A—The A stands for *Application*

K—The K stands for *Kneeling in Prayer*

That all the people of the earth may know

that the hand of the Lord is mighty,

that you may fear the Lord your God forever.

Joshua 4:24

Reflection Question:

The Israelites created a memorial, made of stones, to remind them of how God had helped them.

Do you have something you have held onto as a reminder of how God has helped you?

S—The S stands for **Scripture**

O—The O stands for **Observation**

A—The A stands for **Application**

K—The K stands for **Kneeling in Prayer**

Joshua fell on his face to the earth

and worshiped and said to him,

"What does my lord say to his servant?"

Joshua 5:14

Reflection Question:

Joshua asked the commander of the army of the Lord, what was required of him.

Have you humbled yourself under God's direction? How have you sought out God's will for your life?

S—The S stands for *Scripture*

O—The O stands for *Observation*

A—The A stands for *Application*

K—The K stands for *Kneeling in Prayer*

Keep yourselves from the things

devoted to destruction.

Joshua 6:18

Reflection Question:

God gave Israel victory over a highly fortified city in the most unusual way.

Is there something in your life that seems too difficult to overcome on your own? Perhaps it's time to give the battle to the Lord. Write a prayer today asking God to help you have victory.

S—The S stands for *Scripture*

O—The O stands for *Observation*

A—The A stands for *Application*

K—The K stands for *Kneeling in Prayer*

I will be with you no more,

unless you destroy the devoted

things from among you.

Joshua 7:12

Reflection Question:

Joshua is confused as to why God allowed Israel to be defeated until he is shown that Achan had sinned against God.

Are there things in your life that are holding you back from all of God's possible blessings?

S—The S stands for ***Scripture***

O—The O stands for ***Observation***

A—The A stands for ***Application***

K—The K stands for ***Kneeling in Prayer***

Do not fear and

do not be dismayed.

Joshua 8:1

Reflection Question:

Once the transgression of Achan had been dealt with, God was ready to provide them with a victory.

Name a time, when once you confessed your sin and dealt with the issue, you felt God working in your favor.

S—The S stands for *Scripture*

O—The O stands for *Observation*

A—The A stands for *Application*

K—The K stands for *Kneeling in Prayer*

So the men took

some of their provisions,

but did not ask counsel from the Lord.

Joshua 9:14

Reflection Question:

Despite the fact, that they were lied to, the Israelites still honored their vow of peace.

How does this provide us with a reminder about our own dealings with others?

S—The S stands for *Scripture*

O—The O stands for *Observation*

A—The A stands for *Application*

K—The K stands for *Kneeling in Prayer*

And the sun stood still,

and the moon stopped,

until the nation took vengeance

on their enemies.

Joshua 10:13

Reflection Question:

Joshua prayed a bold prayer of faith. He called out to the Lord, in the sight of Israel, and asked God to make the sun stand still and He did.

Is there something you have been praying for, that you have given up on? Pray a bold prayer of faith today. Watch and see what God does.

S—The S stands for *Scripture*

O—The O stands for *Observation*

A—The A stands for *Application*

K—The K stands for *Kneeling in Prayer*

And the Lord said to Joshua,

"Do not be afraid of them,

for tomorrow at this time

I will give over all of them."

Joshua 11:6

Reflection Question:

After a long battle, there was peace for a season.

Sometimes our journey may be long but at the end, there is always peace when we put God first. How does this bring you comfort in your current season of life?

S—The S stands for *Scripture*

O—The O stands for *Observation*

A—The A stands for *Application*

K—The K stands for *Kneeling in Prayer*

And these are the kings of the land

whom Joshua and the people of Israel defeated...

in all, thirty-one kings.

Joshua 12:7, 24

Reflection Question:

Today we revisited all the kings that God helped Moses and Joshua defeat.

God has helped us defeat many things in our lives. What is one thing God has helped you defeat?

S—The S stands for ***Scripture***

O—The O stands for ***Observation***

A—The A stands for ***Application***

K—The K stands for ***Kneeling in Prayer***

The Lord said to Joshua,

"You are old and advanced in years,

and there remains yet

very much land to possess.

Joshua 13:1

Reflection Question:

Though they still did not have the land, Joshua had to show faith that they would by dividing out the unconquered land to the appropriate tribes.

Name a time that God has had you step out in blind faith. How did it turn out?

S—The S stands for *Scripture*

O—The O stands for *Observation*

A—The A stands for *Application*

K—The K stands for *Kneeling in Prayer*

Caleb said: "My brothers who went up with me
made the heart of the people melt;
yet I wholly followed the Lord my God."

Joshua 14:8

Reflection Question:

Caleb was given Hebron because he believed and trusted God fully even when others doubted.

How does this remind you of your own Christian journey?

S—The S stands for *Scripture*

O—The O stands for *Observation*

A—The A stands for *Application*

K—The K stands for *Kneeling in Prayer*

She said to him,

"Give me a blessing."

Joshua 15:19

Reflection Question:

Achsah had a boldness about her, just like her father. She wasn't afraid to ask Caleb for what she and her husband needed.

Is there something that you need and yet you haven't asked another person or God for it? Do it today.

S—The S stands for *Scripture*

O—The O stands for *Observation*

A—The A stands for *Application*

K—The K stands for *Kneeling in Prayer*

However,

they did not drive out

the Canaanites.

Joshua 16:10

Reflection Question:

Even though the Ephraim tribe received their land, they still did not fulfill God's command and instead kept the Canaanites as slaves.

Is there something you are holding onto, even though God has delivered you out of a bad situation? Today, let's deal with it and let go of it.

S—The S stands for *Scripture*

O—The O stands for *Observation*

A—The A stands for *Application*

K—The K stands for *Kneeling in Prayer*

Then Joshua said to the house of Joseph,

to Ephraim and Manasseh,

"You are a numerous people

and have great power."

Joshua 17:17

Reflection Question:

Joshua has to remind the people of Manasseh that they have great power. They had forgotten all that God had already delivered them from.

Who is someone that is your Joshua, the person who reminds you that you are strong because you are a child of God?

S—The S stands for **Scripture**

O—The O stands for **Observation**

A—The A stands for **Application**

K—The K stands for **Kneeling in Prayer**

So Joshua said to the people of Israel,

"How long will you put off going in

to take possession of the land?"

Joshua 18:3

Reflection Question:

The people had become comfortable with their current condition, so they were not doing anything to claim what was theirs.

Do you find yourself too comfortable to fulfill the plans that God has for you? How can you work towards fixing that today?

S—The S stands for *Scripture*

O—The O stands for *Observation*

A—The A stands for *Application*

K—The K stands for *Kneeling in Prayer*

By command of the Lord

they gave Joshua

the city that he asked for.

Joshua 19:50

Reflection Question:

After all the land was given out, Joshua received his reward.

As a leader, he didn't seek to get the first cut of the land. He waited and he was rewarded with a city. What does this teach you?

S—The S stands for *Scripture*

O—The O stands for *Observation*

A—The A stands for *Application*

K—The K stands for *Kneeling in Prayer*

Anyone who killed a person

without intent could flee there,

so that he might not die by the hand

of the avenger of blood,

till he stood before the congregation.

Joshua 20:9

Reflection Question:

God appointed a place of refuge for those who killed a man without intent. This was his hiding place, from the avenger.

How does this remind you of Jesus and how He cares for us?

S—The S stands for *Scripture*

O—The O stands for *Observation*

A—The A stands for *Application*

K—The K stands for *Kneeling in Prayer*

Not one word of all the good promises

that the Lord had made

to the house of Israel had failed;

all came to pass.

Joshua 21:45

Reflection Question:

Though their journey had been long. God delivered on His promises to His people.

How does this bring you comfort as you are dealing with your current battles?

S—The S stands for *Scripture*

O—The O stands for *Observation*

A—The A stands for *Application*

K—The K stands for *Kneeling in Prayer*

Love the Lord your God,

walk in all his ways

and keep his commandments

and cling to him

and serve him with all your heart

and with all your soul."

Joshua 22:5

Reflection Question:

Now that the people are all settled in, it was important to remind them to continue to love God with all their heart and to continue to follow His commandments.

Has your heart been tempted to stray? How do you stay focused on God through out the day?

S—The S stands for **Scripture**

O—The O stands for **Observation**

A—The A stands for **Application**

K—The K stands for **Kneeling in Prayer**

For it is the Lord your God

who has fought for you.

Joshua 23:3

Reflection Question:

Temptation is always around us. Yet it is important not to allow our temptations to get the best of us.

How do you combat your temptations? Do you have a special friend you can talk with or maybe a special Bible verse that keeps you on track?

S—The S stands for **Scripture**

O—The O stands for **Observation**

A—The A stands for **Application**

K—The K stands for **Kneeling in Prayer**

Choose this day whom you will serve...

As for me and my house,

we will serve the Lord.

Joshua 24:15

Reflection Question:

We are reminded we cannot serve two masters.

Is there something in your life that is standing in the way of you serving God fully today? Make that change today!

S—The S stands for *Scripture*

O—The O stands for *Observation*

A—The A stands for *Application*

K—The K stands for *Kneeling in Prayer*

Made in the USA
San Bernardino, CA
15 August 2016